"Provocative and sensitive, this is a rare publication
that lifts up the issue of "colorism" through a variety of developmentally
and culturally appropriate experiences and explanations. As a person of color
of African descent born in the United States and engaged in
anti-bias and equity work since 1974, I recommend it without reservation."

Ed Greene, PhD
VP, Children, Youth and Digital Media Literacy Initiatives
Hispanic Information and Telecommunications Network (HITN), Brooklyn, NY

"Gupta's language is warm and nourishing, and feels like being spoken to gently
by a person with infinite patience and time for all of our questions. Soak up the
beautiful, evocative illustrations of children and linger on the simple gorgeousness
of the instructive images offered before each activity."

Anastasia Higginbotham
Author/Illustrator, Not My Idea: A Book About Whiteness

"Raising a generation of global citizens is a huge responsibility. It starts with the
words we use, and the stories we choose to tell. Books like Different Differenter are
key to having authentic conversations about diversity and difference."

Sailaja N. Joshi
Founder-CEO, Bharat Babies

"A treasure trove of conversation starters for children and adults, this book skillfully
and thoughtfully engages children in activities that help to answer questions about
identity, culture, colourism and racism that all too often are avoided by parents,
teachers and child advocates. It belongs on the shelves of libraries, classrooms,
after-school programs, and homes where children's inquiring minds can be nourished."

Wendy Luttrell
Professor and Executive Officer Ph.D. Program in Urban Education
and Professor of Sociology and Critical Psychology, The Graduate Center, CUNY, NY

"The book has fun activities and we try new things. I learned how our skin can get darker in the sun. I liked looking at the picture of the map, and I learned about stereotype. It is wrong to treat people differently because they have different colored skin. The book is talking about how our families and friends look different. I have so many friends that look different from me."

Kaashvi
Student, Third Grade, Elementary School

"Many of us see what Jyoti sees, but we are not brave enough to discuss it unless we are in safe spaces. The activities in her eye-opening book pique a child's interest and offers teachers and parents an opportunity to use these teachable moments."

Olga Flores Chen, LCSW
Former school counselor

"Discrimination against dark skin is rampant across class, region and gender. It is important that we engage with children on these issues. I think Different Differenter will trigger many necessary conversations."

Nandita Das
Actor, Director, Activist, and a supporter of Dark is Beautiful campaign

"Jyoti's book speaks to the dual worlds immigrant families often inhabit, maintaining the cultural practices of their ethnic identity with life in the United States. As a Korean-American I wish that her book had been written in the 1970s, when I was in elementary school."

April Kim Tonin
Director of Visual Education, The Nightingale-Bamford School, New York, NY

DIFFERENT
DIFFERENTER

An Activity Book About Skin Color

This book belongs to

Written by Jyoti Gupta

Illustrated by Tarannum Pasricha

CROWDFUNDED BY 100 BACKERS FOR THE COLO(u)RISM PROJECT

Visit www.jyotigupta.com for details.

Writing and design by Jyoti Gupta
Illustrations by Tarannum Pasricha
Cover design by Jyoti Gupta

Published by The Colo(u)rism Project in 2019
The Colo(u)rism Project can be reached at thecolourismproject@gmail.com.

Library of Congress Control Number: 2018908616

ISBN 978-1-7325644-2-8 (hardcover)
ISBN 978-1-7325644-0-4 (paperback)

Printed in the USA

For my son Abir, 5, who resisted pink everything...until he bought
a bunch of roses for his room this spring.

From the author: Parenting is a mix of parents' childhood experiences and culturally informed values woven into daily practice. And yet, I find that our responses to questions about something as fundamental as skin color haven't changed enough. Often, we find ourselves unable to present the historical and cultural nuances in the correct language and tone, leaving our children's simple questions unaddressed.

Different Differenter, a parent-child activity book presents creative modules to facilitate independent thinking among children. It also allows you, the adults to interact with, and experience the child's world through play.

The subjects raised in the book are the result of careful deliberation, readings of scholarly works, and conversations with people across cultures over the last decade. *Different Differenter* is not to be completed in a particular order, although we do encourage you to complete the first module first. Most activities take under an hour and use ingredients and tools available at home. Some are more time-intensive (video), or require supervision (mask making), while others include a wait time between steps (mixed media). The writing activity might be more about timing than time! Get started, and make them your own!

TABLE OF CONTENTS

OUR skin and its COLOR!

Our skin is one of our five sensory organs and it does several things. For instance, it covers and protects our bones and muscles. It also keeps our body temperature the way it should be. The skin on our fingers allows us to feel shapes, materials, textures, and sizes.

Our skin has different thicknesses, and colors. If someone decided to count every shade of skin in the world, which includes many types of browns, blacks and peaches, they wouldn't have any time left to do anything else, not even to sleep or play. Think about fruit skins. Do they have different colors and textures too? What about leaves?

Go for a nature walk and collect 4-5 leaves of different shapes and sizes. Did you notice dark, light, and in-between tones of green? Learn the names of the leaves and different shades of green. Next, make a pattern using the leaves you collected.

❀ STEP 1
Begin by deciding on a color scheme for your artwork. Choose both light and dark colors. Pick a leaf and the lightest color from your paints. Paint the leaf all over, including all the way to the edges. Remember to place the leaf on scrap paper before you paint it, so it doesn't make a mess.

❀ STEP 2
Now press the leaf on your art paper, paint side down, using your hand or a spoon. Be careful not to shift the leaf. Then, lift it gently. Make more impressions with this leaf. Wait for the paint to dry before moving on to the next leaf and a darker color.

❀ STEP 3
You can make cool patterns by using the other leaves. (Remember, always let the paint dry between colors. Wet paints smudge each other and may make your artwork look messy.)

4-5 leaves (wiped dry)   paints + flat brushes   bowl + plate + spoon   art paper + scrap paper

Every person on earth has a different fingerprint. We all have unique tongue prints, too.

SOURCE: Fun facts for your 5-year-old *By Catherine Rauch,*
babycenter.com

ALL the colors in our FAMILY!

Does your skin resemble any of your family members? (It could be its own color or a combination of their skin colors. Sort of like when you mix red strawberries with white milk it turns pink!) Do you have a sibling? Is their skin color like yours or different?

No matter who you look like, you're always adorable, cuddly and lovable!

Ask someone in your family if they would like to help you with a survey about skin colors. If they say yes, bring your book to them and match their skin color to one of the thumbprints on the facing page. Can you find the thumbprint closest to their skin color? *You can write their name under it or draw their face on it. Do the same with all members of your family.*

DO you know WHAT makes skin BROWN?

Did you know hippos don't have to worry about packing sunscreen? Their skin makes a pink slime that blocks the sun.

A magical pigment in our bodies gives our skin its brown color. It's called melanin! If your skin has higher melanin, you will have darker skin, and if your skin has lower melanin, you will have lighter skin. Melanin is also why some people have brown eyes and hair.

The **genes** in our bodies also help decide our skin color. *Genes carry information that makes us look like our parents or grandparents.* They decide which family member we look like the most, or if our hair is curly or straight.

Some people's skin gets darker in the sun. This natural process is called *tanning*. Long hours in direct sun can also give some people a *sunburn* as well as have other harmful effects.

Use the new words you've learned in conversations about skin color, especially if someone does not know them! Discuss healthy *skin care* practices with your family.

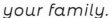

WHY are our SKIN COLORS so DIFFERENT?

We don't know with certainty how many shades of skin existed when the first humans were born. But we do know that they've become more varied over hundreds of thousands of years.

People who lived in places with lots of sunlight produced lots of melanin to block the sun's harmful rays, making them more brown. People in places with less sunlight produced less melanin making them less brown. *This process of slow change is called adaptation, by which humans became more suitable to their environment.*

Animals have also adapted over time. For instance, a turtle can trick others by hiding in its shell and looking like a rock. And a butterfly's colorful wings help it to hide among flowers. Can you think of other animals who can hide or trick others?

Close your eyes. For this activity, think of an animal you want to become today. Follow the instructions to make your own animal mask!

thick paper + scissors

thread (for tying)

black marker + eraser

colored pencils OR crayons

❀ STEP 1
Grab a pencil and measure your face from forehead to chin. Using this measurement make two dots on the paper. Connect them with a straight dotted line. Now measure ear to ear, mark the dots on your paper, and, again, connect them with a dotted line. Make sure the two lines cross at the center. Now draw an oval that connects all four dots.

❀ STEP 2
What is the most prominent feature of the animal you are today? Is it its spots or stripes or whiskers or ears? Draw them. In addition to these, make sure you draw all the features: eyes, nose, ears and mouth. Carefully select the colors of your chosen animal and fill in all the features with the right colors. Choose a color for the face and fill in the remaining parts of the mask.

❀ STEP 3
Ask a grown-up to help you make two tiny holes on each side of your mask for the string and two bigger holes for the eyes. Make sure the eye holes are big enough, so you can see through them. Pull the string through the holes on the sides and tie a knot on one end. Leave the other end long so you can tie the strings behind your head.

The Indian Subcontinent

From water conservation thousands of years ago, to modern solutions in daily living; from natural to human—made beauty, this map has it all.

MAGNETIC HILL

SHEHNAI

DANCING GIRL

JANTAR MANTAR

SKIING

BICYCLING TO WORK

KAZIRANGA NATIONAL PARK

CHAND BAORI

HANDLOOM

SUNDARBANS

DABBAWALAS

KONARK TEMPLE

INDIAN RAILWAYS

KALARIPAYATTU

SCUBA DIVER

ORIENTAL SWEETLIPS

GALLE LIGHTHOUSE

WHAT does our SKIN COLOR tell others about US?

Nothing, really! However, our skin color, along with our name, the languages spoken at our home, as well as our special festivals and holidays, might tell others a little about our family's way of life.

Some people believe they can tell things about a person by looking at, or talking to them. But really, they're using *stereotypes* to make a guess. *A stereotype is an untrue belief that many people have about all people or things with a particular characteristic.* An example of a stereotype is that girls have long hair or boys like blue. (You know that's not true.) Remember, the more information we learn, the more we know and understand the world around us.

Look at the map on the facing page. Did you know the first people to settle in the Indian subcontinent lived more than 5,000 years ago? Research the places, things, people, animals, and actions on the map. Like when they were built, why they're important, or their relationship with their environment.

Ask your parents where they are from? Where are you from? Is it where you live, where you were born, or where one (or both) of your parents were born?

✿ Step 1
Spread light molding paste evenly on a thick sheet of paper and let it dry. Paint over it with reddish-rust acrylic paint and leave it to dry. Or you can make your own clay batter by mixing 2 tablespoons terracotta clay, 2 tablespoons water, and 1 tablespoon Elmer's glue or Fevicol. Make sure the batter is neither runny nor too thick. It should coat the paper in a thin layer. Test it on a piece of paper. Once you've got the right texture, spread the batter evenly on your art paper. Do not leave any white spaces. Dry in the sun or under the fan.

✿ Step 2
While your sheet is drying, practice drawing Warli figures. Also practice the final artwork you have decided to draw. Next, take a white color pencil and draw your artwork on the coated paper.

✿ Step 3
Once your drawing is complete, paint the final artwork using a thin brush and white paint. Wait for it to dry. Finish the unfinished fine parts with a white color pencil.

Our families are different in many ways. A friend or their grandparents might speak a different language. Some friends might bring food, or carry backpacks, or wear clothing that we might not be familiar with. Or maybe a friend has a name that sounds different from other names. These are details that tell us about our friend's cultural background.

Have you noticed the toys and books in your friend's home? Or other decorative and artistic objects? Learn where these things are from when you visit next time.

Wall painting is a popular way to decorate homes in many cultures. The people of Warli, a region in the Gujarat-Maharashtra region, create special mud walls and paint groups of people (and animals) dancing or working on the walls. *Observe the Warli-style drawings on the page. Make an artwork representing yourself, or your favorite activity, or toy in Warli-styled art!*

thick art paper

terracotta / molding paste

sharp white colored pencil

paint + thin brush + glue

HOW
are our
FAMILIES
different?

*WARLI ART IS THE CULTURAL INTELLECTUAL PROPERTY OF THE TRIBAL COMMUNITY!

IS FOOD a part of our CULTURE?

Yes, it is! And what's more, the same type of food, whether bread or dessert is made in different ways in different parts of the world.

Did you know ice cream was made in Greece, Persia, and China around the same time, and each culture had an original recipe? Although these recipes are nearly 2,000 years old, they are used to this day.

A popular dessert in the Indian subcontinent is the *laddoo.* People use similar ingredients like wheat, millet, or gram flour, sugar, a variety of dried nuts and seeds, and oil or butter. The mixture is then shaped into balls. Each type of laddoo has a unique taste, texture and aroma (smell of food). *Ask your friends to describe their favorite dessert. Now make laddoos using dates.*

25-30 dates

3 tablespoons dried nuts

1/2 cup grated coconut

bowls + plate + spoon

✽ **Step 1**
With clean hands, split the dates and remove the seeds. Use your fingertips to mash them into a smooth pulp. Transfer the pulp to a large bowl.

✽ **Step 2**
Mix 4 tablespoons of your favorite dried nuts into the pulp. Using the spoon, separate the mixture into equal portions and place them on a plate.

✽ **Step 3**
Roll each portion between your palms and shape them into balls. Now roll them in grated coconut. Serve cold.

HOW can we TALK about OUR differences?

We notice different things about our friends: how they look (their hair, their skin color) and how they sound (their language or their accent). If something about a friend makes you curious, it's best to ask a teacher or someone in your family about it first. Remember, making comments about others can hurt their feelings. Did that ever happen to you? What did you do?

Remember, ask good questions, the ones that won't hurt your friend's feelings. And just like asking good questions, it's important to ask them in the right manner; that shows you're trying to learn something new. If your comment hurts a friend, say sorry. If someone says something that hurts you, please let them know how you feel.

Just as people have physical differences, they also have unique personalities: funny, quiet, talkative, shy. Can you guess the children's feelings on the facing page? *Draw, or write and perform a poem or a short story describing how you feel about looking different.*

Grown-ups, at times, find it difficult to make friends with people that look or sound different from them. Want to know what history teaches us about that?

A few hundred years ago some grown-ups divided people into groups, and made special rules that helped one group while ignoring others. For instance, in the Indian subcontinent they divided people into *castes,* such as 'lower,' 'upper' and 'outcastes' (or Dalits). Similarly, in some places, they divided people into *races*, such as Brown, Black, Indigenous or White races. Some of these castes and races became bossy, saying that the other castes or races were less smart than them. This made the others unhappy, and unsafe. Until, one day, they fought and defeated the bossy ones.

Even today, people who believe that caste or race decide a person's ability, don't play or work with that person. Do you think that's right? Remember, we can stop such people. (Maybe *you* can give them a history lesson.) We need to remind them that everyone is equal. And amazing things happen only when we do them together.

What are some actions that seem wrong with the image on the facing page? Mark them with an 'x.' Discuss how you can stop adults from bad behavior.

Why are GROWN-UPS sometimes MEAN to EACH OTHER?

LEARNING DIFFERENCE SPOT WHAT'S WRONG

WHAT can we do when SOMEONE'S MEAN to us?

Children can be mean to each other, sometimes on purpose, and sometimes when we're unable to control our emotions. One way to avoid behaving like that is to think about how we're feeling, and how that is affecting our emotions and actions.

Let's imagine the picture on the page is a drawing of your classroom. A new student has joined your class. Two other students are talking about and making fun of the new student, while a third is trying to scare her with a toy spider. These are examples of bullying. *A bully is a person who does mean things to people because they like to pretend they are stronger or better than others.* The new student is sad.

Design a poster or record a 1-minute video about why bullying is wrong.

LEARNING DIFFERENCE POSTER / VIDEO

HOW can WE make things BETTER?

Talking to friends and adults is a brave and smart way to fix a problem at school or in the neighborhood.

Just like when you share a new song you learned, a game you played, or a funny joke, in the same way, if a classmate is rude to you, talking to someone you trust is a good next step.

Now ask an adult to participate in a role play activity! Ask them to be the child and you be the parent! Tell the adult to pretend that they came back from school feeling sad because another child in the school tried to bully them. Have a discussion with them. What can you say to them to make them feel better?

paints + brushes

art paper + pencils + eraser

palette (to mix colors)

water (to rinse)

CHILD ADVOCATES HAD PROPOSED THIS ACTIVITY
AND SOME EDUCATORS WERE CONDUCTING IT
IN THE U.S. IN THE 1970S.

LOVING DIFFERENCE SELF-PORTRAIT

Let's MIX PAINTS to make our BEAUTIFUL shade of BROWN!

Do you remember how old you were when you first drew a family portrait? Maybe your parents do.

Do you know if you draw yourself, that drawing is called a self-portrait? *A self-portrait can look either exactly like you, almost like you, or it can even represent you in an imaginary way, made of shapes and objects.*

Make a realistic self-portrait, one that looks like you. Practice mixing paints to match your skin color, and not use ready-made crayons or paints. Did you know all skin colors can be made using the three primary colors (red, blue and yellow) in different proportions?

❋ STEP 1
Draw your face including your eyes, nose, lips, teeth, ears and hair. We will return to these features, namely eyeballs, the eyebrows, the lips and the hair, at the end.

❋ STEP 2
Begin by mixing 4-5 drops of red and yellow each. Then add a drop of blue and see how the color begins to change to brown. With the help of an adult, see when you reach the right tone of brown that looks like your skin. To make it lighter, mix in a little white; to make it darker, mix in a little blue.

❋ STEP 3
Paint the color of your skin on the paper in the shape of your face. Remember to leave some space unpainted for eyes, lips, teeth. Next, paint the eyeballs, the eyebrows, the lips and the hair and finish your artwork.

UNIQUE means there's JUST one like ME?

Sometimes we show off our toys and clothes to impress others. But, really, tt's not the things we own that make us unique; it's our personality. *Your personality is the combination of things you like, your habits, and behavior.* Think about the people you love, or with whom you enjoy spending time. Is it because of who they are or the things they have?

Sometimes we want to buy something because we see it in an advertisement. *An advertisement,* **also called an ad or a commercial,** *is a very short story about a thing or an experience that we can buy.* Remember, when we watch an advertisement we forget what we already have and focus on what we don't. We can't possibly own everything we see.

Analyze the elements of the ad on the facing page, such as text, photograph or drawing, and logo. Do you think they are telling the truth? *Can you go through the maze without buying anything?*

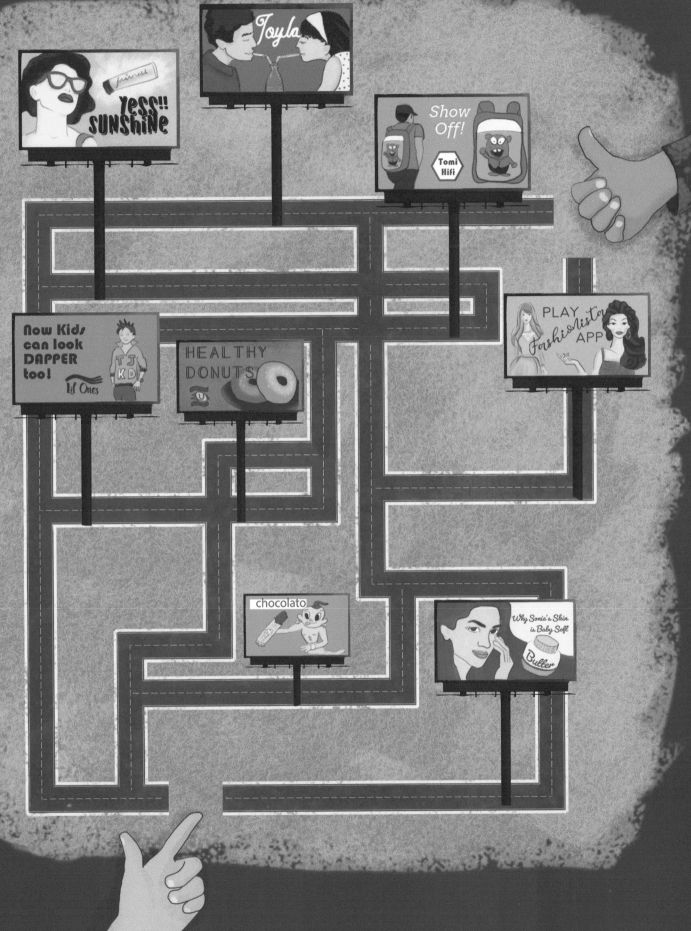

WHAT do we LOVE about OURSELVES?

What is original and unique about you? Is it what you like talking about, or what you like doing, or how you solve problems?

Sometimes we try to be like our friends, or act like someone on our favorite show. Or we try to behave like our parents and elder brothers or sisters, or someone we saw on our way to school, because who doesn't want to be like grown-ups? But what really makes us special is that no other person is exactly like us. Even what makes us sad is unique about us.

Think. "What makes me afraid and what makes me excited and what makes me sad? What do I like to do for fun? What new skills do I enjoy learning the most?" Now make a collage of people, objects, or activities you love, dislike, want to do... things that make you, you!

colored paper + scissors

pencils + colored pens

magazines + newspapers

glue + bowl

GLUE

Happy

Times

FASTEST
CARS EVER

LOVING DIFFERENCE PAPER COLLAGE

ACKNOWLEDGMENTS

An idea is only as strong as the people who get involved. *Different Differenter*, a multidisciplinary, exploratory, scholarship-based, creative project is the result of a community's wholehearted and selfless contributions.

Thank you, elementary educators, for your unabating spirit. And for transmitting values of love and kinship year after year after year. Thank you, early educator Ambreen Satia; visual artist and art teacher Jasmeet Khurana; radical media scholar Saswat Pattanayak; literacy and life skills expert Professor Dr. Mridula Seth; urban designer Sabina Suri; and gender and social development advisor Rie Debabrata Tamas. You brought your extraordinary disciplinary lenses to this book.

Thank you, Professor Parameswaran at the Media School, Indiana University Bloomington, for spelling out what colorism in our part of the world looks like. Thank you, professors at The Graduate Center, CUNY, for pointing me to some, and distilling some seminal texts.

Thank you 100 backers, for turning an idea into a book. Thank you, Qusai, Aarti, and Sheemita, for starting a daisy chain of conversations with parent and child advocates. Thank you, women and moms of color, for supporting the book, for unpacking your childhood memories, for your vulnerability, and for your strength.

Thank you, Kristina S. Spritzer, for fanning the fire. Thank you, Aruna Viswanathan, for always stimulating me. Thank you, Manali Shah, for the shot in the arm this past year.

Thank you Kumar, for helping me live my truth. Thank you, Ma and Papa, and Sis, for teaching me *how to see*.

JYOTI GUPTA

Jyoti is from Old Delhi, 'the heart' of India's capital city. After working as a print designer in the advertising industry, and watching new-age, regressive T.V., she decided to quit it all to chase her dream of studying, and pursuing a career in media studies. Sure enough, a few moons later, she founded The Colo(u)rism Project and completed several media projects successsfully.

Jyoti conducts workshops and presentations in Delhi and the U.S. serving various age-groups and audiences. She lives in New York with her spouse, 5-year old son, and his imaginary cat Daisy.

TARANNUM PASRICHA

Tarannum majored in Applied Art at the College of Art, Delhi, and followed it up with a filmmaking course at the University of Southern California. Although a filmmaker by day, she illustrates regularly on her days off. Tarannum loves experimenting with various techniques, materials, and media. She and her sister recently co-published an illustrated book of their mother's poems. She has worked on social films advocating child rights, alongside regular adverts she calls "selling soap."

CPSIA information can be obtained
at www.ICGtesting.com
Printed in the USA
LVHW071050251021
701183LV00028B/704